The fun way to learn!

Sarah Watts

kevin mayhew

kevin mayhew

First published in Great Britain in 2002 by Kevin Mayhew Ltd
Buxhall, Stowmarket, Suffolk IP14 3BW
Tel: +44 (0) 1449 737978 Fax: +44 (0) 1449 737834
E-mail: info@kevinmayhewltd.com

www.kevinmayhew.com

This edition © Copyright 2002 Kevin Mayhew Ltd.

The music in this book is protected by copyright and may not be reproduced
in any way for sale or private use without the consent of the copyright owner.

ISBN 978 1 84003 875 0
ISMN M 57024 004 3
Catalogue No. 3611631

Cover design: Rob Mortonson
Music setting: Donald Thomson
Proof reader: Marian Hellen

Printed and bound in Great Britain

Contents

	Score	Part
A change in the weather	24	7
Advent calendar	34	11
Anna Lou	8	2
A.S.A.P.	14	4
Blue sock blues	10	3
From Pineapple	18	5
G's garden	36	12
Katie's room	12	3
Little flower	20	6
Psychedelic	32	10
Still waters	23	7
Stormy	6	2
Three way	30	9
Too late for Jane	17	4
Tortoise jive	28	8
Waltz on West 79th Street	27	8

Acknowledgement

For Michèle Turner who 'bowed' these pieces, and whose technical advice was much appreciated. Thank you.

A note from the composer

This is a fun book of jazzy pieces with a 'feel good' accompaniment to encourage you in the early stages of learning.

Although *Razzamajazz* is not a tutor, I hope you will enjoy learning the pieces and benefit from them.

SARAH WATTS

STORMY

© Copyright 2002 Kevin Mayhew Ltd.
It is illegal to photocopy music.

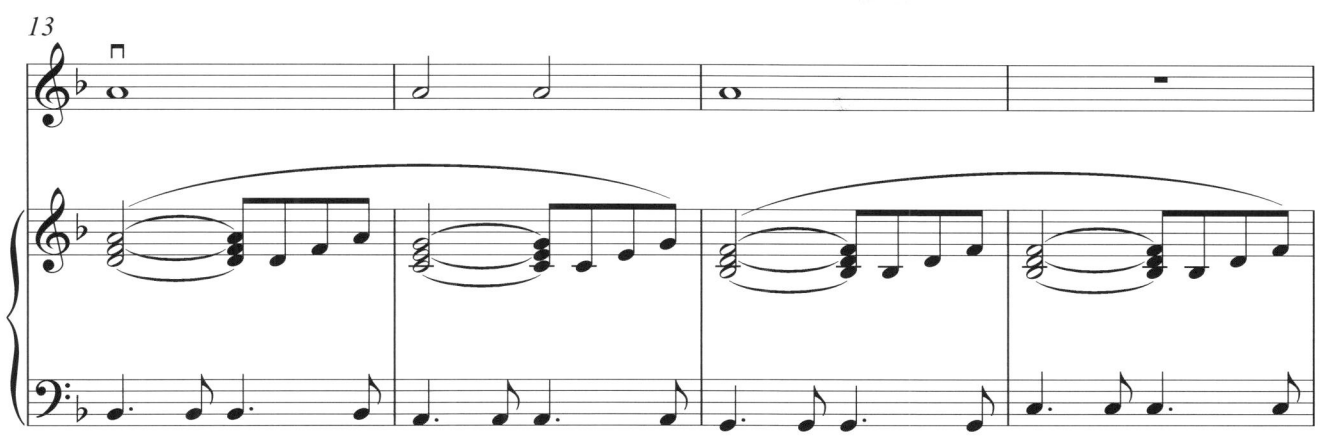
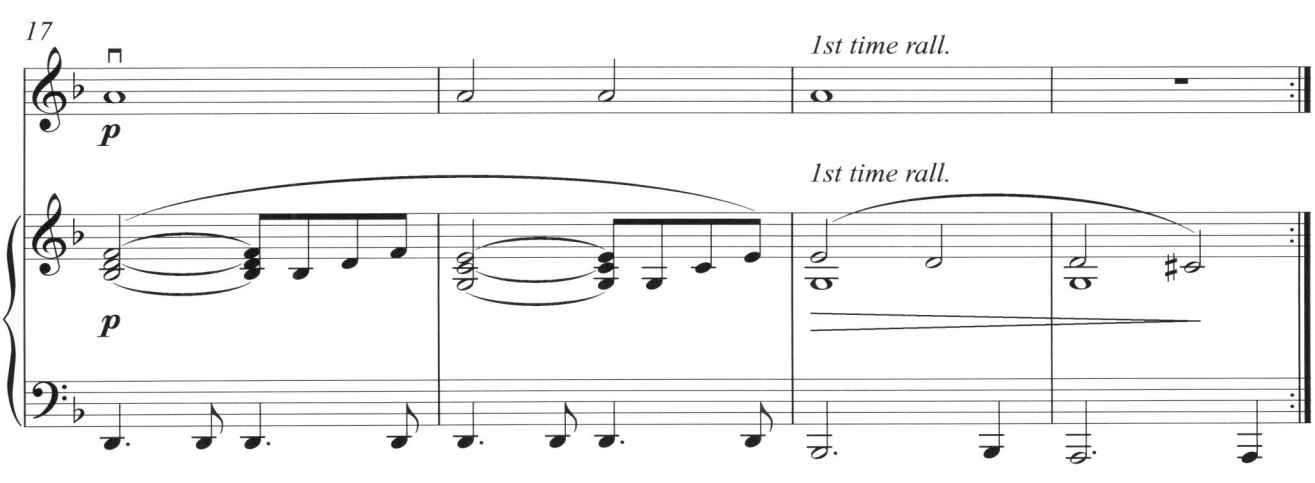
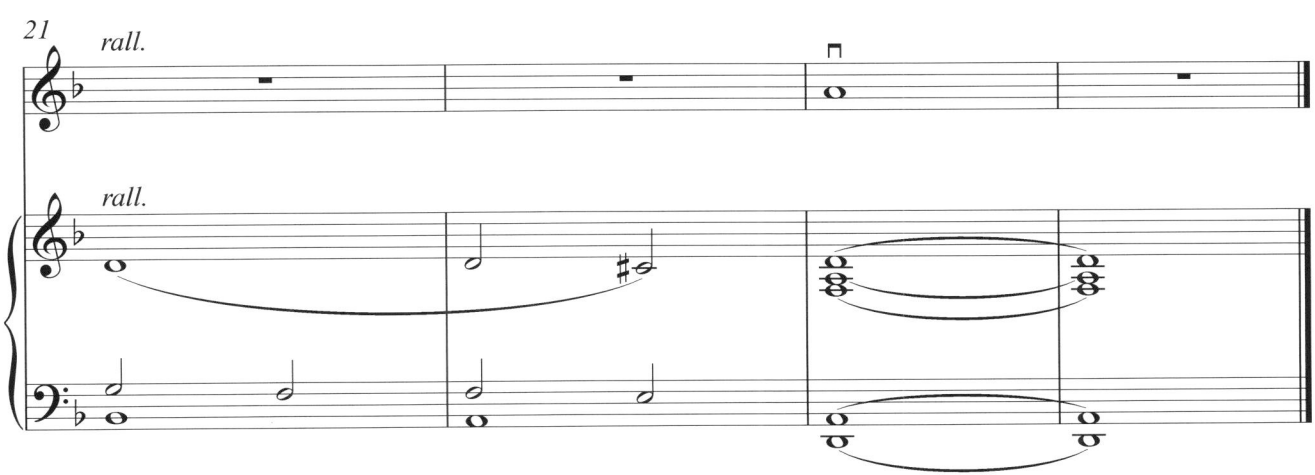

for Anna Cashman

ANNA LOU

for Chloe Shrimpton

BLUE SOCK BLUES

© Copyright 2002 Kevin Mayhew Ltd.
It is illegal to photocopy music.

KATIE'S ROOM

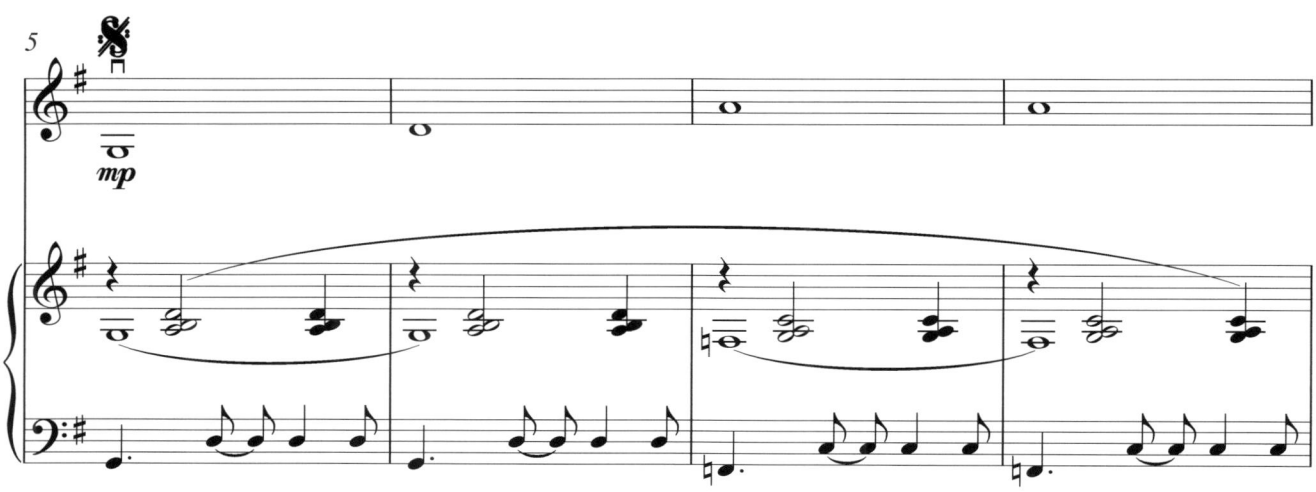

© Copyright 2002 Kevin Mayhew Ltd.
It is illegal to photocopy music.

A.S.A.P.

TOO LATE FOR JANE

FROM PINEAPPLE

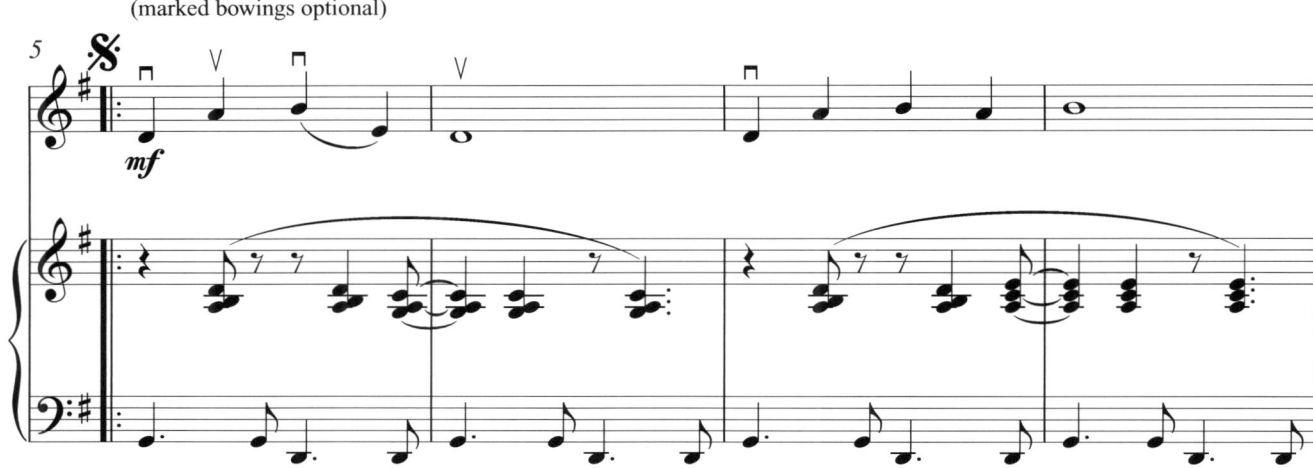
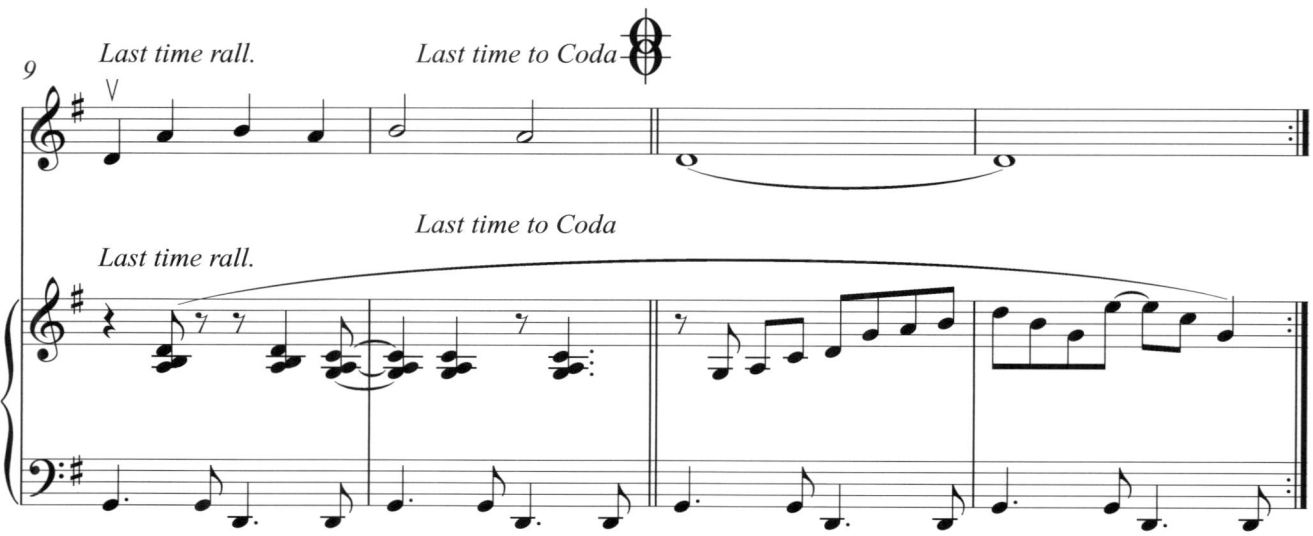

© Copyright 2002 Kevin Mayhew Ltd.
It is illegal to photocopy music.

LITTLE FLOWER

Sarah Watts

STORMY

for Anna Cashman
ANNA LOU

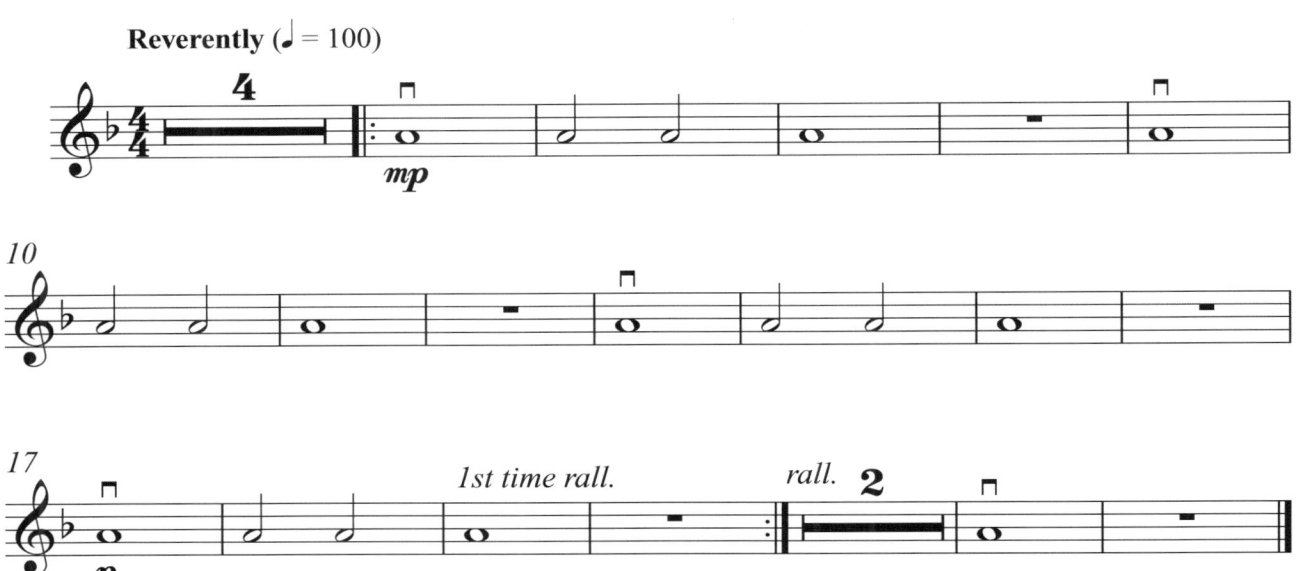

© Copyright 2002 Kevin Mayhew Ltd.
It is illegal to photocopy music.

for Chloe Shrimpton

BLUE SOCK BLUES

KATIE'S ROOM

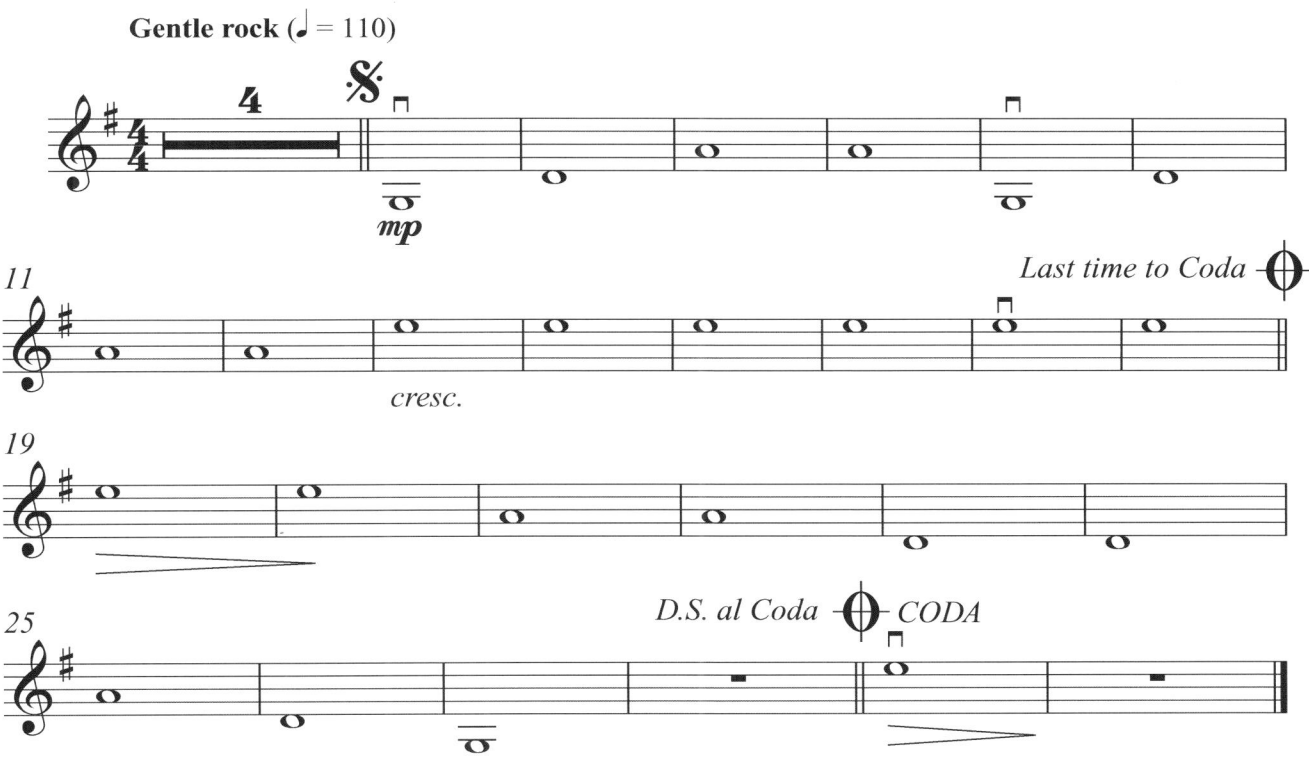

© Copyright 2002 Kevin Mayhew Ltd.
It is illegal to photocopy music.

A.S.A.P.

TOO LATE FOR JANE

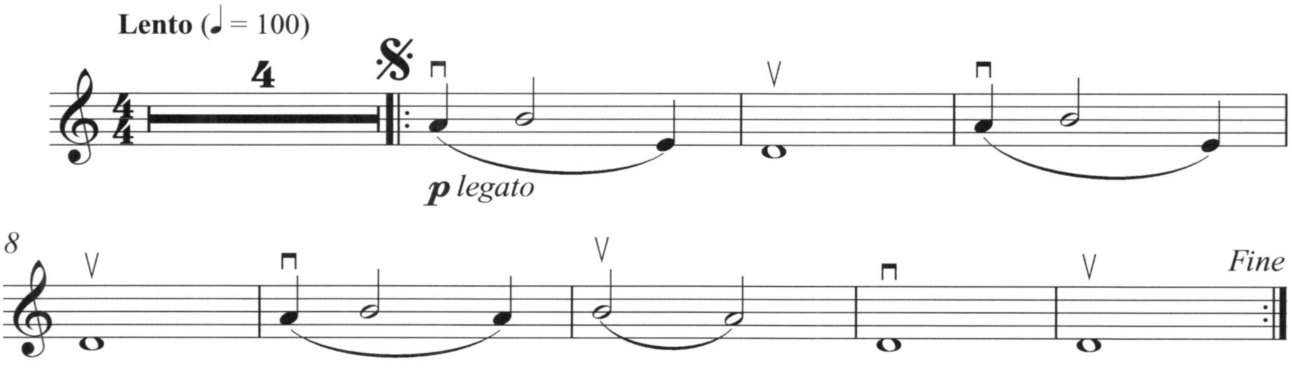

© Copyright 2002 Kevin Mayhew Ltd.
It is illegal to photocopy music.

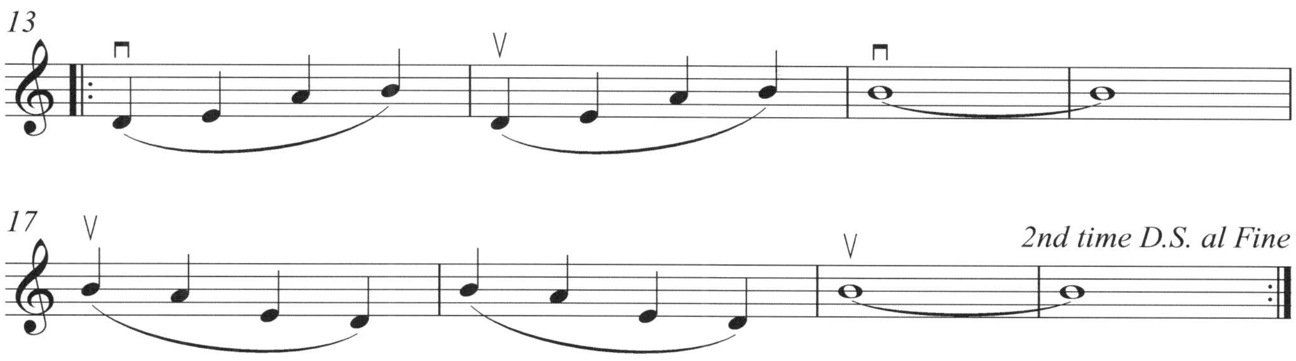

FROM PINEAPPLE

Light latin (♩ = 110) (marked bowings optional)

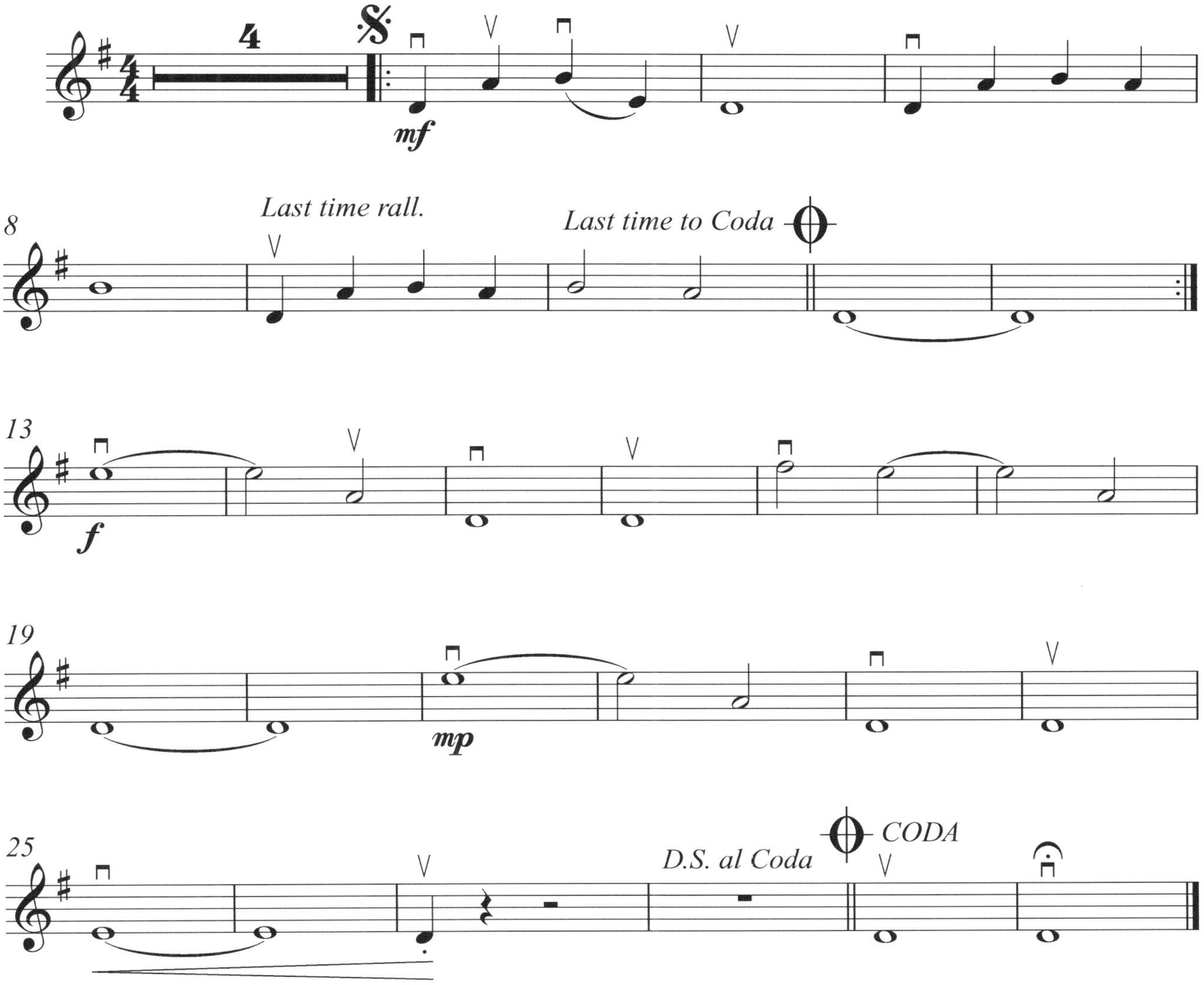

LITTLE FLOWER

STILL WATERS

A CHANGE IN THE WEATHER

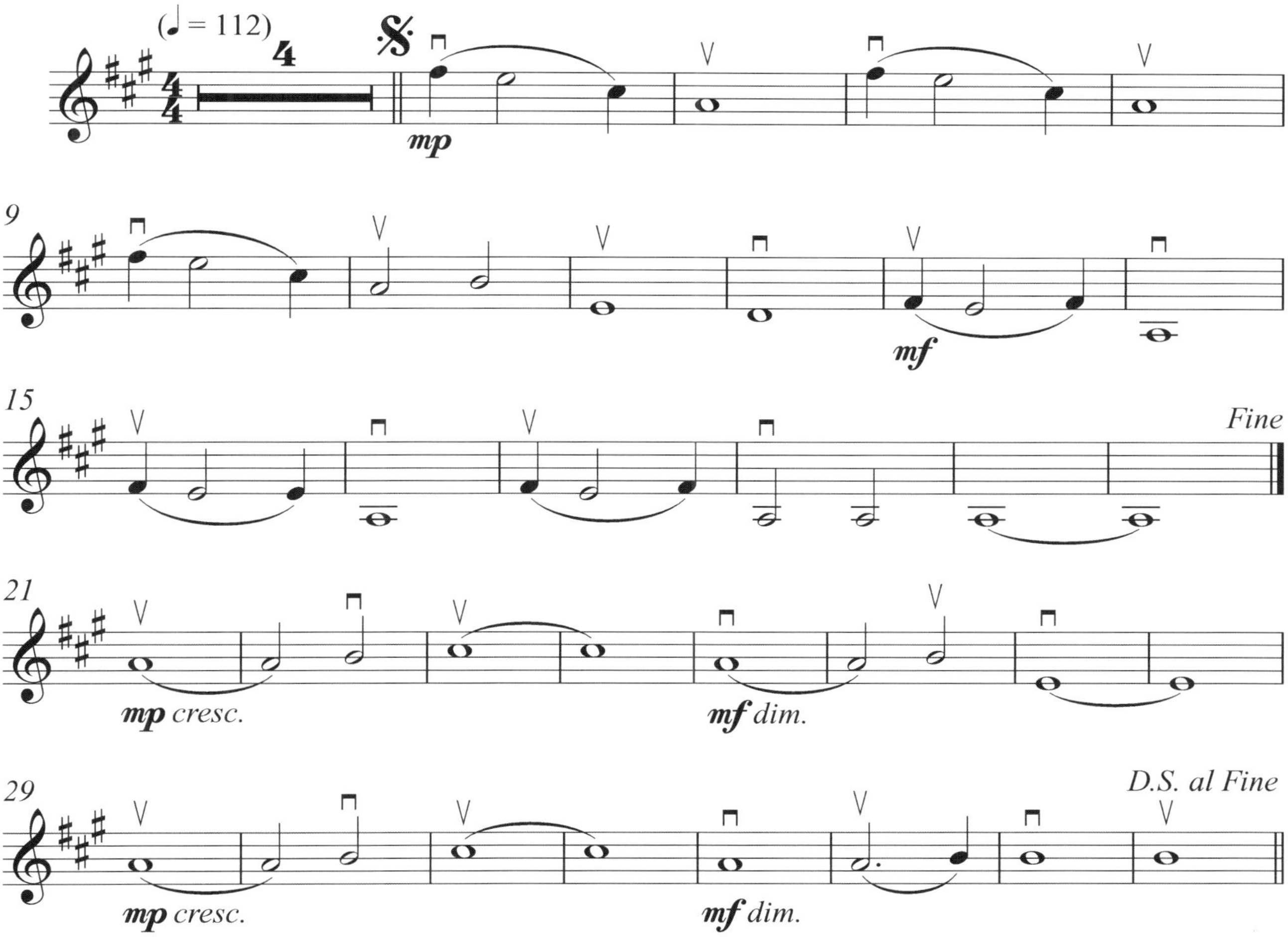

© Copyright 2002 Kevin Mayhew Ltd.
It is illegal to photocopy music.

WALTZ ON WEST 79TH STREET

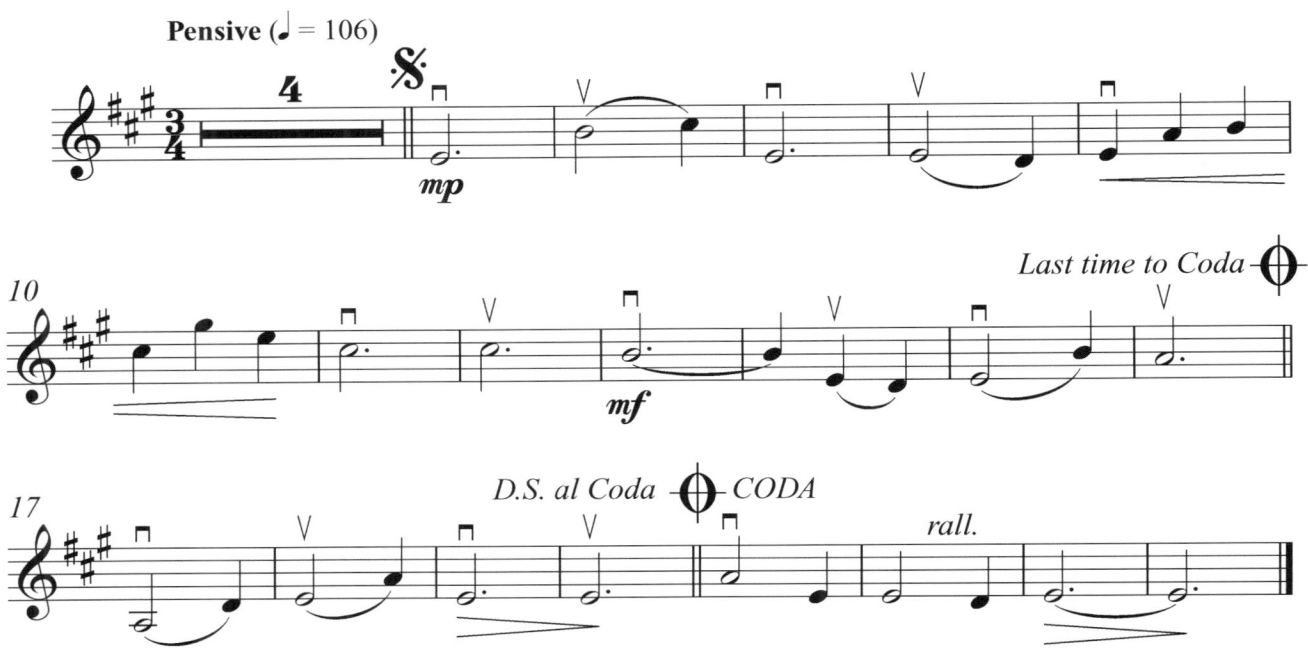

for Martha Shrimpton

TORTOISE JIVE

© Copyright 2002 Kevin Mayhew Ltd.
It is illegal to photocopy music.

THREE WAY

© Copyright 2002 Kevin Mayhew Ltd.
It is illegal to photocopy music.

PSYCHEDELIC

Hold bow in hand while playing pizzicato

60's rock (♩ = 120)

Ooh!

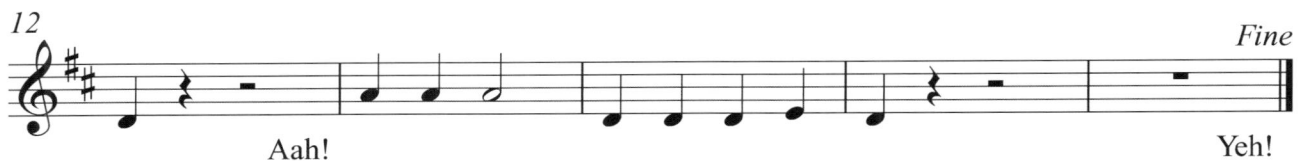
Aah!   Yeh!

                                                                    Ooh!

                                                                    Aah!

                                                                    Yeh!

© Copyright 2002 Kevin Mayhew Ltd.
It is illegal to photocopy music.

ADVENT CALENDAR

© Copyright 2002 Kevin Mayhew Ltd.
It is illegal to photocopy music.

G'S GARDEN

STILL WATERS

© Copyright 2002 Kevin Mayhew Ltd.
It is illegal to photocopy music.

A CHANGE IN THE WEATHER

WALTZ ON WEST 79TH STREET

© Copyright 2002 Kevin Mayhew Ltd.
It is illegal to photocopy music.

for Martha Shrimpton
TORTOISE JIVE

© Copyright 2002 Kevin Mayhew Ltd.
It is illegal to photocopy music.

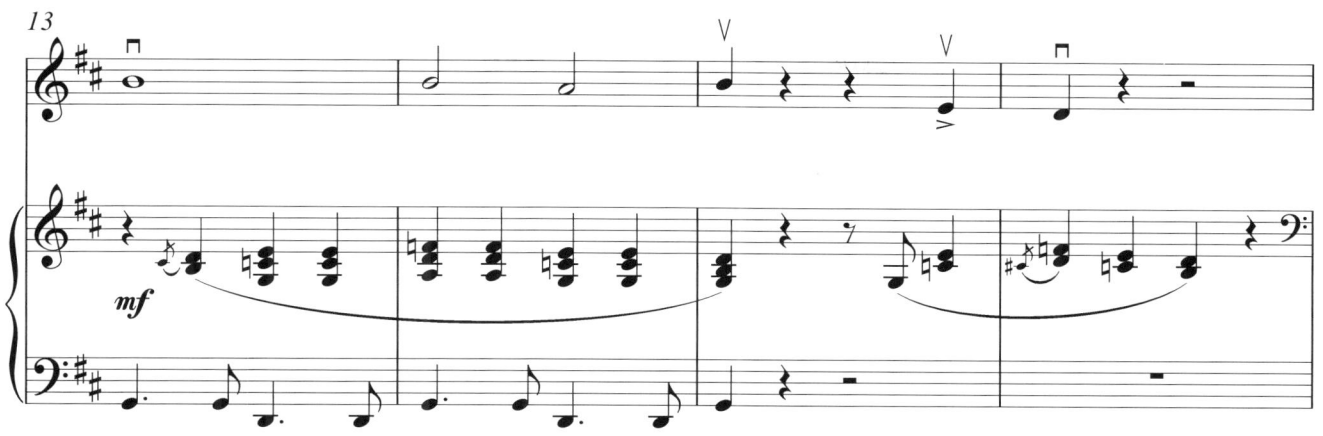

THREE WAY

PSYCHEDELIC

© Copyright 2002 Kevin Mayhew Ltd.
It is illegal to photocopy music.

ADVENT CALENDAR

Light rock (♩ = 110)

© Copyright 2002 Kevin Mayhew Ltd.
It is illegal to photocopy music.

G'S GARDEN

You'll also enjoy

Class Act for Violin
3612050

Favourite Celtic
Melodies for Violin
3611542

Favourite Spirituals
for two Violins
3611545